Frankl's "Big Itch" Fieldbook

as told to Philip Ramsey

Pegasus Communications, Inc.
Waltham

Acquiring editor: Kellie Wardman O'Reilly
Project editor: Lauren Johnson
Design: Robert Lowe and Lainie Rutkow
Production: Nancy Daugherty
Cover and interior illustrations: Robin Runci Mazo

♻ Printed on recycled paper.
Printed in the United States of America.
First printing August 1998
ISBN 1-883823-29-3

For additional copies or information on volume discounts, contact:
Pegasus Communications, Inc.
One Moody Street
Waltham, MA 02453-5339
Phone: 781-398-9700
Fax: 781-894-7175
www.pegasuscom.com

5052

04 03 02 01 00 99 98   10 9 8 7 6 5 4 3 2 1

Contents

Publications by Pegasus Communications, Inc.

Hey—welcome to my Big Itch Fieldbook! I hope you enjoyed reading how Billibonk and I solved the problem of the elephants' itch. I loved this adventure. For Billibonk, though, the itch made it less than thrilling! Still, despite his discomfort, he was glad that he learned more about how to find real solutions to his problems. This Fieldbook is designed to help you to use the same lessons Billibonk learned to investigate the problems that bug you.

Just like the Thorn Patch Fieldbook that accompanied *Billibonk & the Thorn Patch*, the first story about Knith, this Fieldbook uses the Big Itch story to get you to think about a particular problem that affects you or your work group. I'll give you questions to think about, and there are some diagrams to help you further. Whenever possible, try to work with colleagues on the questions and exercises in this book—the more you can do this, the richer your insights will be.

The last Fieldbook introduced the idea of interconnectedness—it described some of the complexities of making decisions and showed how communities can learn together. In this Fieldbook, we'll explore a common systemic structure affecting the way individuals and groups solve problems. The structure is called "Shifting the Burden." As you'll see, this systemic structure created a pattern of problems that the elephants had trouble understanding. Once they grasped it, though, they saw their itching problem in a whole new light. Rather than treating the itching problem as if it were a one-time event, they looked at the whole system in which they

> ### ❧ Systemic Structure
>
> When I talk about "systemic structure," I mean the way the parts of a system are arranged. It's this structure that produces patterns of behavior. Structure can refer to *anything* that shapes behavior in a system—from the physical layout of a thorn patch, to the attitudes of community members.

were living, and identified how its very structure was causing them problems. With this new way of thinking, they were able to get rid of their itching *and* make sure that it didn't come back.

It can be hard work exploring questions about your problems. You may even feel like blaming other people for the difficulties. That's a very normal reaction. If you see yourself doing it, have a little laugh at yourself, apologize to the others, make a mental note that you tend to do that when you're under pressure, and carry on. The idea is to use this Fieldbook to explore new insights together, in a way that will help you and the people you work with.

Happy learning!

—Frankl 🐾

Problem, or Symptom?

When Billibonk and the rest of the elephant herd woke up itchy, they knew they had a problem. If you asked the elephants what their problem was, they would likely have said, "We're itchy."

Answering a question in this way, though, can create a serious difficulty for the problem-solver: confusion between problems and symptoms. A problem is a set of circumstances that create an undesirable situation. Often these circumstances aren't obvious to those involved. A symptom, on the other hand, is obvious—it's something that tells you that you have a problem. With the elephants, the itch was a symptom that let them know they had a problem—a bug infestation that was going to bring lots more scratching in the future.

Symptoms are very useful because they let you know you've got the problem in the first place. And, because symptoms make you feel bad, having them motivates you to take actions to fix the problem (see Figure 1).

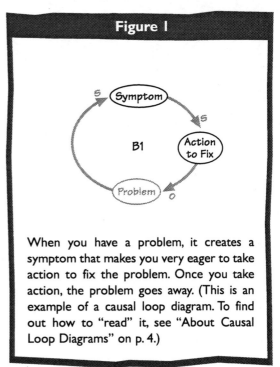

Figure 1

B1

Symptom

Action to Fix

Problem

When you have a problem, it creates a symptom that makes you very eager to take action to fix the problem. Once you take action, the problem goes away. (This is an example of a causal loop diagram. To find out how to "read" it, see "About Causal Loop Diagrams" on p. 4.)

🐾 About Causal Loop Diagrams

Causal loop diagrams, or CLDs, are graphic depictions of systemic structures. The diagrams consist of variables connected by arrows that show the movement of feedback throughout the system. Each arrow is labeled with a sign ("s" or "o") that indicates how one variable influences another. Here's an example of a simple CLD:

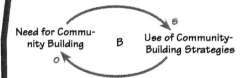

In this diagram, need for community building and use of community-building strategies are the two variables connected by feedback arrows. The "s" on the upper arrow means that when the level of need for community building changes, the use of community-building strategies changes in the *same* direction. For example, if the need increases, the use of strategies also increases. The "o" on the lower arrow means that when use of community-building strategies changes, then the level of need for community building changes in the *opposite* direction. For instance, as use of strategies increases, the need decreases.

Causal loop diagrams are made up of a combination of balancing and reinforcing loops. The simple CLD is an example of a balancing loop, as indicated by the "B" in the center. A balancing process tends to keep the system behavior relatively steady overall. In our example, for instance, the two variables balance each other and keep each other under control. A reinforcing process, by contrast, drives change in one direction with even more change. Reinforcing processes are recognizable by the uncontrolled or exponential change that they create. The figure below, labeled "R," is a simple example of this kind of dynamic.

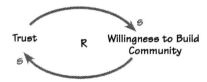

In this reinforcing loop, each arrow is labeled with an "s" for same direction of change. To read this diagram, you would say that "as trust increases, so does the willingness to build community, which leads to even more trust."

Balancing and reinforcing processes occur in infinite combinations in the systems we see all around us, including behavior within organizations.

✌ Is Pain Good or Bad?

Pain—whether physical or emotional—is something we all experience at times. But is pain good or bad? When asked this, some people say, "What a silly question; of course pain's bad." Others say, "What a silly question; of course it's good." Why this difference in answers? It may have something to do with whether you think more about how pain *feels* or about what it *does*. Pain feels bad. What it *does*, though, can be very good. For example, once I injured my front leg stepping on a thistle. After that, I felt pain whenever I put pressure on that leg. Because the pain felt bad, I tried to avoid it by taking most of my weight on my other three legs. Putting less strain on my injured leg let it heal itself more quickly. In this case, there was a good outcome that happened because the pain felt bad.

So, pain—or any other symptom—can be both good and bad. What matters most is what you do when you notice the symptom.

What's *Your* Problem?

❓ How do you know when you have a problem within your organization? There are probably many different "signals"; list as many as you can below. Feel free to brainstorm responses with colleagues.

❓ Look back at what you listed. Which things tell you that something is wrong? By definition, these are symptoms. Circle a symptom that you and your work group would like to explore further. Keep that symptom in mind as you answer the questions throughout the rest of the Fieldbook.

Quick Fixes:
Making the Symptoms Go Away

As we saw in the Big Itch story, symptoms are useful because they let you know you have a problem, and they motivate you to do something about it. The trouble with symptoms, though, is that they can often lead you to use what's called a symptomatic solution: getting rid of the symptom without really fixing the problem. When you do this, the symptoms almost always come back again later.

The elephants experienced this with their itch. Scratching made the itch feel better—for a bit. Likewise, the lotion that the monkeys mixed up for them stopped the itching for a while. But scratching and using lotion were just symptomatic solutions, or "quick fixes"—they only treated the symptom (the itch) and not the real problem (the bugs), as shown in Figure 2. Because the bugs were still there, it was just a matter of time before the itch would start up again.

We mice face similar sorts of problems. Imagine that you are a mouse living in Knith. Snakes are dangerous to mice—and the sooner we learn how to handle them, the safer we are! Fortunately for

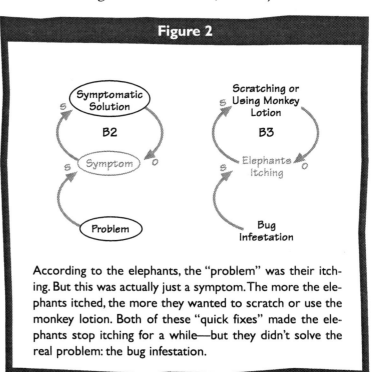

Figure 2

According to the elephants, the "problem" was their itching. But this was actually just a symptom. The more the elephants itched, the more they wanted to scratch or use the monkey lotion. Both of these "quick fixes" made the elephants stop itching for a while—but they didn't solve the real problem: the bug infestation.

us mice, snakes smell. The smell of a snake makes your nose tingle, like the start of a sneeze. Though the feeling is not very pleasant, it is very handy for detecting when there's a snake around.

But when snake-hatching time comes, "snake-stink" is everywhere. It seems that your nose is constantly twitching and tingling. You may be tempted to block your nose with something to keep out the foul snake odor. But this "solution" could have grave consequences. . . .

What's Wrong with Treating the Symptom?

? Think about what could happen if you took a "block your nose" approach to your work problems. Write your ideas in the space below.

? Think about the symptom you circled on p. 5. While you may not know what makes the symptom keep coming back, you've probably got a good idea of how people (including you) try to get rid of it. Below, list some of the quick fixes that you and others have tried.

Uncovering the Real Problem

Generally, quick fixes don't work because they don't make the real problem go away. They just hide it for a while. The trouble is, problems are often invisible. When we see a symptom, it tells us we have a problem. But, what problem? Confusion about how to define the real problem is one reason that quick fixes—which only treat the symptom—are so appealing. Usually, everyone finds it easy to agree on the symptom. The elephants all knew they were itching—in fact, the whole jungle of Knith knew!

In the story, Billibonk and I tried to uncover the real problem by repeatedly asking "why?" Each time we asked, we got closer to identifying the problem. Why the itch? Too many bugs! Why too many bugs? Not enough birds! Why not enough birds? Too many ants! Why so many ants? Bad nest-building . . . and so on. Usually, by the time you've asked "why" five times, you have a clearer picture of the real problem.

This kind of questioning can be a very powerful tool. When you see something that needs fixing, before you jump into fixing it, ask yourself, "Why has this happened?" To answer this question, you'll have to do some investigating. When you have found the cause behind what happened, ask yourself, "Why did this causal event occur?" (and so on, as you keep digging deeper).

Later in this Fieldbook, you'll have a chance to try this technique. Before you do, though, there are a couple of important investigative ideas you should know about.

Going Disconfirmational

One thing that gets in the way of a good investigation is a habit that most people have. It's a habit that seems as though it should work. The trouble is, it doesn't. The habit is looking for evidence to confirm our ideas. Imagine that you and I have an argument over something. I decide that you are being unreasonable. In fact, I decide that you are an unreasonable person. From then on, I notice times when you are unreasonable. Strangely enough, these episodes will be easy to spot because (1) I'm looking for them, which may irritate you into acting "unreasonably," and (2) I'm around. It may be that you get into arguments only with me, but those are the times I see you. Therefore, every time those episodes occur, I confirm my suspicion that you are, in fact, unreasonable. As you might guess, explaining the argument this way suits me fine.

A better idea is to look for evidence to *disconfirm* our ideas. To test whether you are an unreasonable person, I could look for times when you are reasonable. I could ask others how they view you, or watch how you get along with them. Often we make up our minds about things without ever looking for proof that our ideas are wrong.

One way to test our ideas is to look for things that stand out as different. In the elephant herd, Honka was different because he wasn't as itchy as the rest of the herd. That difference was a key to understanding what caused the itch. Rork and Ella were different from the other bug-birds: They stayed in the jungle when the others left. Finding that out helped Billibonk and me to discover the real cause of the elephants' itching— and to design a real solution to the problem.

What's Different About *Your* Problem?

❓ Think about the symptom that you and your colleagues identified earlier. Who suffers from it?

[?] Who else might you also expect to be suffering, but doesn't seem to be?

[?] What's different about that person?

A Word of Warning: Sometimes there may be a number of things different about a particular person, and we could focus our attention on the wrong difference. Honka, for instance, superstitiously believed that the reason he wasn't itchy was that he was big. While his bigness may have made him more attractive to the bug-birds, we could have taken a wrong turn in the investigation if we had focused on his bigness as the only reason for his not being itchy.

The Problem with Blaming

When you are investigating a problem, you are sure to run into another common obstacle: blaming. You'll ask, "Why did this happen?" and someone will say something like, "It's Jane's fault. Things always go wrong when she's in charge!" Running into blaming is like running into a rhinoceros—it brings the investigation to a sudden (and painful!) halt. It's tempting to think that the purpose of an investigation is to find out who is to blame. That way, we can punish that person and feel like we've taken action. Often, though, we have to choose between punishing people and solving the problem. And, if people are afraid of being punished, they may not give us the information we need to find out what's going on.

In *Billibonk & the Big Itch,* you saw how quickly the elephant herd blamed Billibonk for their itch. But the blaming led to a troublesome end: Once the elephants decided that the itching was Billibonk's fault, they stopped looking for a solution! Fortunately, Billibonk was up to the challenge of continuing with the investigation—despite the extra pressure from the herd.

If you are investigating a problem and people are blaming each other for it, try asking them to suggest other reasons for the problem, or for why people acted the way they did in the first place. It can be valuable to ask questions like, "Why do we think things go wrong when Jane's in charge?" or "If things go wrong when Jane's in charge, why isn't she learning from her mistakes?" or "Why did we put Jane in charge?" A good investigation helps you get beyond explanations that treat the problem as a one-time event, and shows how the system itself may be structured in a way that actually creates problems.

Investigating *Your* Problem

Think again about the symptom you identified earlier, and use the worksheet that follows to find the problem that's causing it. This might take some time. At each stage, you and your group will do a fresh round of investigation, perhaps talking with various people and testing your ideas in different ways.

On the worksheet, I've called the problem symptom a "provocation," because it is what provokes the investigation. The answer to each "why?" then becomes a new provocation—stimulating either a new round of investigation or, at the end, some action that may finally solve the problem.

Problem-Identification Worksheet

Provocation #1:

"Why" Question:

The symptom probably occurs because:

How tested:

Provocation #2:

"Why" Question:

The symptom probably occurs because:

How tested:

Provocation #3:

"Why" Question:

The symptom probably occurs because:

How tested:

Provocation #4:

"Why" Question:

The symptom probably occurs because:

How tested:

Provocation #5:

"Why" Question:

The symptom probably occurs because:

How tested:

The Likely Problem:

Did You Notice Any Blaming?

Throughout the above investigation, you probably ran into some blaming behavior. You'll have noticed it, for sure, if it was directed at you! Here are some questions to help you think further about blaming.

? What are some examples of blaming that occurred during the investigation?

? What effect did the blaming have on your investigation?

? How did you and your group get past the blaming?

? Did any of the accusations being leveled at you or others in your group turn out to actually be part of the likely problem you identified?

Waiting for Results

One of the most appealing things about solutions that treat just symptoms is that they work so fast. That's why they're called "quick fixes." The wonderful thing about scratching an itch is how much better you feel right away. This happened with the elephant's other anti-itch quick fix, too: the monkey lotion. The "medicine" made Billibonk and his friends feel better immediately.

Fixing the real problem takes much more time than fixing the symptom. As you can see in Figure 3, there are two sources of delay. First, investigating the possible sources of a problem takes time. So, once you have spotted the symptom, there is a delay before you know what action to take. Second, the action often takes a while to kick in. (To fix the elephant's itch, for example, we had to carry out an elaborate egg-hatching scheme that involved lots of waiting.)

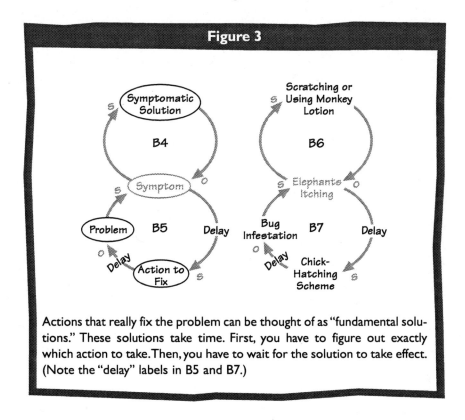

Figure 3

Actions that really fix the problem can be thought of as "fundamental solutions." These solutions take time. First, you have to figure out exactly which action to take. Then, you have to wait for the solution to take effect. (Note the "delay" labels in B5 and B7.)

So, when you're trying to address a symptom, you have two choices. One option is to take a quick-fix action, which makes the symptom go away while leaving the problem intact. This option is shown in the upper loops in Figure 3. We can think of these sorts of options as *better before worse*. Because they address just the symptoms, they make things *feel* better for a while. The root problem still exists, though, so the symptom soon comes back. And because the problem has been allowed to grow, the symptom often comes back worse than it was before.

Alternatively, you can investigate the symptom to find the real, or fundamental problem causing it, and take action to address this problem. This decision is shown in the lower loops in Figure 3. This is the harder choice, because it involves investigating without blaming, testing your ideas, and tolerating delays that make things feel worse while the problem is being fixed. We can think of these actions as *worse before better*. When you address the real problem first, the delays cause the symptom to get worse for a while, until the treatment takes effect. Once the problem is fixed, though, the symptoms go away for good. Then you *really* feel better!

Sometimes it's possible both to treat the symptoms and fix the fundamental problem at the same time. The elephants did this when they simultaneously used the lotion and waited for the egg-hatching scheme to work. As we'll see shortly, this can be dangerous, so it's a strategy you have to use with care.

Usually, because a fundamental solution can take so long to design and implement, people are tempted to keep resorting to the quick fix. This tendency to choose quick fixes over fundamental solutions is very common. It's called "Shifting the Burden," because in effect we shift the burden of solving the problem onto the quick fix and away from the fundamental solution. "Shifting the Burden" is a common systemic structure that occurs everywhere: from jungles to companies to families.

Delays in *Your* Problem Investigation

? On p. 13, you identified a probable cause for the symptom that has been troubling you. You may already have ideas for how to fix the problem properly. Use the space below to list possible sources of delay in fixing the problem. Try estimating the length of the delays, too.

? During times of delay, what is likely to happen to the symptom?

? If the symptom gets worse, who will be affected, and how?

? What action could you take to help those affected cope with the impact of the delays?

Side-Effects of Quick Fixes

ne of the best things about fundamental solutions is that they help you avoid some nasty side-effects that many quick fixes have. As you know, our actions often have unintended, undesirable consequences. An action intended to make you feel better can set off a chain of events that only makes you feel worse in the end. Quick-fix actions are notorious for having unpleasant side-effects that aren't at all intended by the people taking the action. In the first part of Figure 4, you can see how the symptomatic solution, or quick fix, leads to the side-effect.

Figure 4

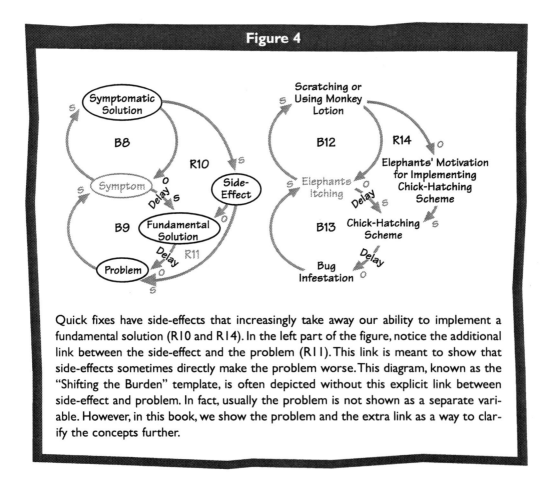

Quick fixes have side-effects that increasingly take away our ability to implement a fundamental solution (R10 and R14). In the left part of the figure, notice the additional link between the side-effect and the problem (R11). This link is meant to show that side-effects sometimes directly make the problem worse. This diagram, known as the "Shifting the Burden" template, is often depicted without this explicit link between side-effect and problem. In fact, usually the problem is not shown as a separate variable. However, in this book, we show the problem and the extra link as a way to clarify the concepts further.

A particularly troublesome side-effect of a quick fix is that the motivation to address the fundamental problem gets reduced. Remember, symptoms motivate us to take action. It makes sense, then, that a quick fix that takes the symptom away also takes away a lot of the motivation to fix the fundamental problem. For example, when an elephant like Billibonk gets itchy, his main interest in life is finding a cure for the problem. If something takes the itch away—like scratching the itch or using the monkey's lotion—an elephant may find that he has time to think of more pleasant things, like eating. Finding a cure for the itch no longer has the same urgency.

A key thing to remember about these side-effects is that, the more they happen, the less we're able to implement a fundamental solution. Notice in both parts of Figure 4 that the side-effects become part of a reinforcing process. This reinforcing process actually forms the final "piece" in the "Shifting the Burden" structure—every "Shifting the Burden" situation has an upper balancing loop that contains the symptomatic solution, or quick fix; a lower balancing loop containing the fundamental solution; and a reinforcing process containing the impact of the quick fix's side-effect.

In the second part of the figure, let's trace the action as it moves through the system, to see how the reinforcing process gets activated: The more the elephants resorted to scratching or using lotion to get rid of their itch, the less motivated they were to figure out a fundamental solution to

the problem (note the "o" link in loop R14). As their motivation dwindled, so did their ability to design and implement the chick-hatching scheme (note the "s" link). But the longer the chick-hatching scheme got delayed, the more the itch kept coming back, which prompted the elephants to use the quick fixes even more, thereby reducing their motivation for the fundamental solution even more—and so on.

Reduced Motivation in Your Own Problem-Solving

❓ Think of a time when you saw someone's motivation to solve a problem disappear because of a quick fix. Describe the situation below.

❓ Have you seen quick-fix approaches to the symptom you circled on p. 5? If so, describe the effect the quick fixes have had on motivation to address the symptom's underlying cause.

Over-Helping

*L*ike me, I'm sure you've had the experience of watching others struggle to do something that you could do easily. I've sometimes watched young mice struggling to open a seed-pod—the equivalent, I guess, of young humans struggling to tie their shoe laces. It's obvious that the others' lack of skill is frustrating for them. It can also be painful for you to see something done badly when you feel sure you know how it should be done. So, it's tempting to say, "Here. Let me do that for you." But is this really being helpful?

Struggling is a *symptom* of a lack of skill. When we take over and do things for someone who's struggling, that is a kind of quick fix. Though taking over can make the immediate frustration go away (for both you and the other person), the problem of frustration is sure to come back again. The person still hasn't learned the skill, and won't be able to draw on it the next time he or she needs it. Every time Billibonk has asked for my help, I've been careful not to do everything for him. That way, he learns more and can use his learnings the next time a problem comes up.

Taking time to learn a needed skill also has some important, positive side-effects. As people experience the struggle to learn new things, they build up a tolerance for the effort involved. Then, when they try something else new, they will be prepared for the effort required and feel ready to work through the struggle.

If we don't allow others to experience the struggle of learning, we rob them of this important lesson. Over time, they will become intolerant of tension. They may give up on projects unless they can complete them quickly. They grow less able to put up with the delays in developing and implementing fundamental solutions.

Naturally, when we over-help, we think we're doing good. We may, however, be taking away the other person's ability to cope with tension—an ability required by anyone who wants to learn or create anything new. This situation is a variation on "Shifting the Burden," and is sometimes called "Shifting the Burden to the Intervener," because one person who has responsibility (a burden) shifts it onto a helper.

I don't mean to say that helping others is a bad thing—it isn't! If it weren't for the help I've had from other animals, I'd have been snake-food long ago. There is an important distinction to be made, though, between helping people handle their responsibilities, and taking their responsibilities from them. In a healthy community, people will generally learn to take on more and more responsibility, *not* less and less.

Do You Over-Help?

? In the space below, describe a time when you helped someone in such a way that you made it easier for them to avoid learning something.

? Describe something you have avoided learning to do by getting others to do it for you.

? Note some examples of situations in your organization where people regularly shift their learning burdens onto others.

? One of the odd things about "Shifting the Burden to the Intervener" is that it soon starts to feel normal. People begin to think, "Why should I have to do that difficult job, if someone else can?" This seems to happen often where there is someone who looks well qualified and happy to accept the responsibility. Try adding your own examples to the list of "Shifting the Burden to the Intervener" statements below:

"Why should I have to teach my children? That's what teachers are for!"
"Why should I have to worry about my health? That's what the doctor is for!"

Addiction

U p 'til now, we've been talking about a quick fix as something that is easier to do than finding a fundamental solution to a problem. Sometimes a quick fix becomes more than that, though. People feel *compelled* to opt for a quick fix—even when it's clear that it's bad for them. This is Addiction, another variation on the "Shifting the Burden" theme.

We all hear about and experience many kinds of addictions. Often addictions occur when we look for some artificial way of feeling good quickly, rather than go through the drawn-out process of making the deeper, longer lasting changes needed to have a rewarding life. Addiction is an especially nasty side-effect of quick-fix solutions and "Shifting the Burden." Like any side-effect, it reduces our motivation to search for a more fundamental solution. But it also leads to actions that are really harmful. Addiction to alcohol, for instance, can result in heavy drinking that harms the drinker's health, relationships, and finances. These only add to the problems that started the drinking in the first place.

Addiction in *Your* Organization

❓ Are there any destructive activities commonly used by people in your organization? Describe them below.

▟ Choose one of the destructive activities that you'd like to explore further. Work through the "five whys" (see p. 12) to find the root cause of this activity, and note your conclusion below.

▟ Is there any addictive behavior associated with the problem you investigated on p. 12? If so, describe it here.

▟ Sometimes addiction is allowed to continue because the addict doesn't have to confront the consequences of destructive behavior— other people clean up for him or her. How might the addictive behavior you described above be confronted?

Combining Fundamental and Quick Fixes

Sometimes the symptoms of a problem are so painful they have to be treated immediately, to give you time to sort out the fundamental problem. The elephants experienced this with their itch. Because the egg-hatching scheme took a while to work, the elephants needed some quick "pain relief" in the form of the monkey lotion. Even so, the herd established some rules for ensuring that they didn't become dependent on the lotion or lose motivation for the egg-hatching plan, the fundamental solution.

So, if you are planning some action to address the fundamental problem behind troublesome symptoms, decide whether you want to use a quick fix at the same time. If you decide that you do need some pain relief, find a way to ensure that you and others don't become addicted to it.

Can *You* Use Some Pain Relief?

❓ Think again about the problem you identified on p. 13. If the people involved in addressing the problem have to go without pain relief while waiting for a solution to take effect, what is likely to happen?

? What forms of relief would you recommend to "hold people over" while they investigate possible solutions and then wait for the solutions to take effect?

? How can you make sure you and your colleagues don't develop the side-effect problems of addiction or loss of motivation for solving the real problem as you explore the problem you identified?

Important Practice

One of the best ways to really understand the ideas we've been discussing is to teach someone else. This someone can be anyone, though it's best if he or she knows less about quick fixes and "Shifting the Burden" than you!

So, for practice, read *Billibonk & the Big Itch* with a child, and see how much you can learn together from the story. Here are some tips.

Share the Reading

Depending on the ability of the child you're reading to, take turns reading paragraphs from the story. A fun alternative is to share the animals' voices—the child could say everything one character says, and even use a funny or strange voice if he or she chooses. Some children find the comments in the boxes used throughout the story distracting. If this is the case, just skip past them. The child may enjoy rereading the book later, including these comments.

Ask Questions

Every now and then, ask questions to encourage the child to compare the characters' experiences with his or her own. Don't worry about asking questions after each chapter; some children may simply want to find out how the story ends. If the child gives an answer you didn't expect, accept it, or perhaps say, "I can see why you might think so. Another reason could be . . ." Be careful not to say, "But . . ." too much—this is something Billibonk had to learn in the story.

Shown below is a question you could ask the child for each of the chapters:

1. How do you think Billibonk felt when Cody blamed him for the itch?
2. What do you think is making the elephants itchy?

3. Have you ever had a problem that was so annoying you couldn't think straight about what to do? What do you do to help yourself think when this happens?

4. Do you say "but" too much? Do I? What could we say instead of "but"?

5. What do you think is the difference between a sign of the problem and the real problem?

6. What do you think of Honka's theory that being big keeps you from getting itchy?

7. What do you think bug-birds have to do with the elephants' itch?

8. What do you think about asking the birds why they think the elephants are itchy?

9. Can you explain how ants in the birds' nests cause elephants to be itchy?

10. What could the animals of Knith do to get more bug-birds in the forest?

11. Do you think the elephants' threats to ask Billibonk to leave the herd will make Billibonk work harder to solve the itching problem?

12. Why do you think Billibonk was so happy to have Chekup's help?

13. Even though Frankl couldn't quite build the bird's nest in the tree, how did this experience help him anyway?

14. Why does Frankl think Ella will keep laying eggs?

15. Why is Billibonk unhappy about having to wait so long for the egg-hatching scheme to work? Have you ever had to wait a long time for something that you wanted very much? What was it like?

16. The monkey lotion is much quicker than the egg-hatching scheme. Why do you think Frankl doesn't like the elephants' using the lotion?

17. Do you like working hard to get something done, like Ella seems to?

18. Why did Ella say that helping can be a trap? Is it a good idea to help others? How can you do it without getting into a trap like the monkeys did, where you can never stop helping?

19. Why did the itch come back after the elephants had used the lotion?

20. What did you think of the story?

A Goodbye

I hope that the questions in this Fieldbook produced some helpful insights for you and that using Billibonk's adventure was a valuable way to generate ideas for addressing problems in your own organization. If you have other ideas about how to use *Billibonk & the Big Itch*, or if something in the Fieldbook worked particularly well for you, I'd love to hear about it. Because contact with Knith is often unreliable, you might go through Phil Ramsey by email at the following address: P.L.Ramsey@massey.nz.